This book belongs to

....

Illustrations copyright © 2018 Kari Stileman
Copyright © 2021

make believe ideas ltd

The Wilderness, Berkhamsted, Hertfordshire, HP4 2AZ, UK.

www.makebelieveideas.co.uk

Photographs courtesy of Shutterstock.

Llama's
busy week

by Rosie Greening

make
believe
ideas

Get the most from this reader

Before reading:

- Look at the pictures and discuss them together. Ask questions such as, "What is Llama doing here?"

- Relate the topic to your child's world. For example, say: "Do you like dancing? Why?"

- Familiarise your child with book vocabulary by using terms such as *word*, *letter*, *title*, *author* and *text*.

During reading:

- Prompt your child to sound out unknown words. Draw attention to neglected middle or end sounds.

- Encourage your child to use the pictures as clues to unknown words.

- Occasionally ask what might happen next, and then check together as you read on.

● Monitor your child's understanding. Repeated readings can improve fluency and comprehension.

● Keep reading sessions short and enjoyable. Stop if your child becomes tired or frustrated.

• •

After reading:

● Discuss the book. Encourage your child to form opinions with questions such as, "What did you like best about this book?"

● Help your child work through the fun activities at the back of the book. Then ask him or her to reread the story. Praise any improvement.

On Monday, Llama paints.
"I love painting,"
says Llama.

On Tuesday, Llama swims.
"I love swimming,"
says Llama.

On Wednesday, Llama surfs. "I love surfing," says Llama

On Thursday, Llama dances.
"I love dancing," says Llama.

On Friday, Llama kicks.
"I love kicking,"
says Llama.

On Saturday, Llama drives. "I love driving," says Llama.

On Sunday, Llama sleeps.
Llama says nothing!

Discussion Questions

1. When does Llama dance?

2. Does Llama swim in a pool or the ocean? How can you tell?

3. Do you think Llama was tired on Sunday? Why?

✌ Sight Words ✌

Learning sight words helps you read fluently. Practise these sight words from the book. Use them in sentences of your own.

says

busy

day

on

week

love

I

LL4M4

⋑ Rhyming Words ⋑

Can you find the rhyming pairs?
Say them aloud.

day

kick

lick

swim

way

him

sleep

peep

paint

faint

dive

drive

Writing Practice

Read the words, and then trace them with your finger.

love

say

swim

kick

paint

sleep

27

❦ Silly Sentences ❦

Have fun filling in the gap in each
sentence. Use the ideas below
or make up your own.

On Saturday, I ....

I love ....